Harsimran

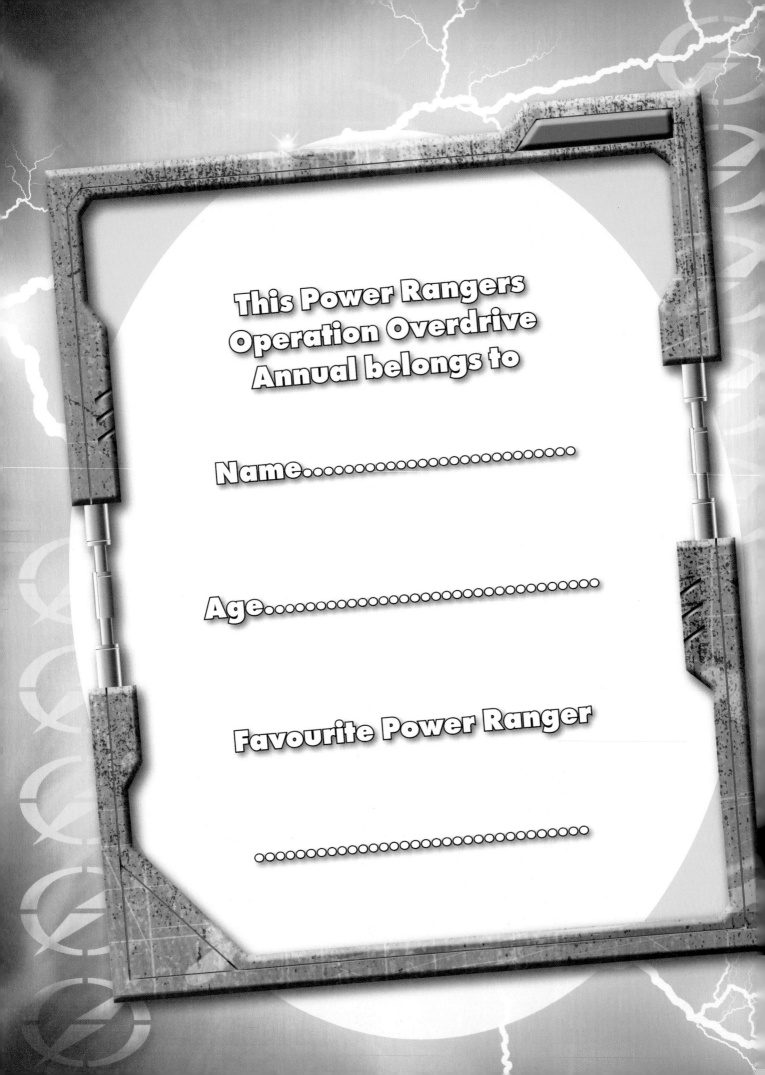

This Power Rangers
Operation Overdrive
Annual belongs to

Name..

Age...

Favourite Power Ranger

....

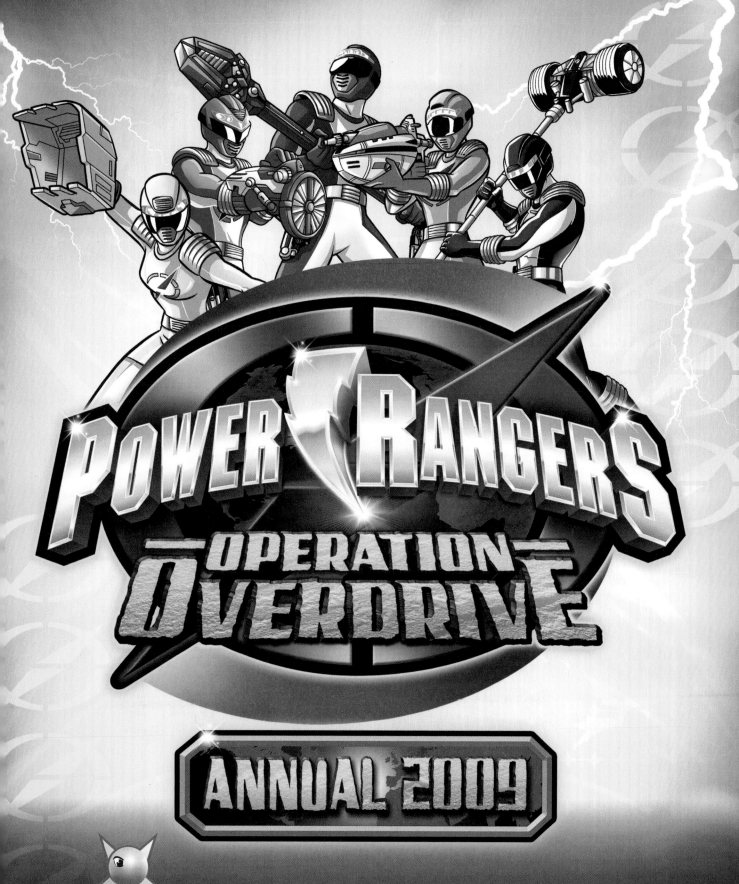

POWER RANGERS
OPERATION OVERDRIVE
ANNUAL 2009

EGMONT
We bring stories to life

First published in Great Britain 2008 by Egmont UK Limited
239 Kensington High Street, London W8 6SA
Edited by Jo Strange Designed by Colin Treanor
ISBN 978 1 4052 3902 8
10 9 8 7 6 5 4 3 2 1
Printed in Italy

CONTENTS

CALLING ALL RANGERS!

Welcome to your action-packed Operation Overdrive Annual! It's time to power up and help the latest team of incredible Power Rangers with their mission: to protect the Corona Aurora from evil forces!

Inside, you'll find exciting comic stories, fact-filled Ranger profiles, plus cool puzzles and quizzes to really test your Ranger ability. Let's go!

OVERDRIVE OVERVIEW

Spencer, the long-serving butler to the Hartford family, has kept a secret diary of his time working for the amazing billionaire adventurer, Andrew Hartford. This is the first entry...

SPENCER'S DIARY

Dear Diary,

Let me begin by saying what a pleasure it is to commit these thoughts to paper with the proper instrument - namely, a sturdy, correctly weighted fountain pen furnished with a gold-tipped nib. I hear that the trend these days is to write everything electronically. So no doubt I will be accused of being old fashioned by not creating a - I believe the word is - "blog" for this record. But so be it. If nothing else, there are issues of secrecy to consider, and any butler worthy of the name knows he must be discreet at all times.

Had Mr Hartford's discovery of a certain crown remained secret, then perhaps this diary would not be necessary. However, that was not possible, given the nature of the treasure he had unearthed. It was perhaps the most startling discovery ever made on Earth ... even though I suspect an equally great treasure may shortly be revealed, of which more later.

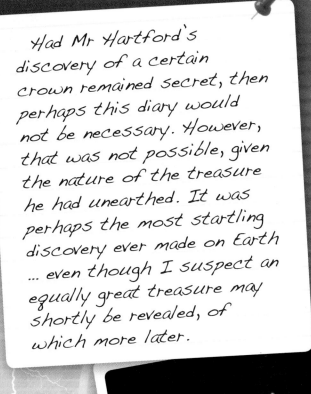

The crown, discovered on one of Mr Hartford's many exploration trips abroad, was correctly identified as the Corona Aurora. Alien in origin, it contained settings for five fabulous jewels. It is said that whoever wore the crown in its complete version would become the most powerful being in the universe.

Unfortunately, such power had earlier attracted the attention of those bent on evil. Two brothers in particular, Flurious and Moltor, had been very keen to capture the Corona Aurora. They were thwarted by the Guardian of the Crown, also known as the Sentinel Knight. He had banished the wicked pair to distant planets, then hidden the crown on Earth and scattered its five jewels across the planet to prevent its power from falling into the wrong hands.

For centuries, the Corona Aurora lay undiscovered, while Flurious and Moltor slumbered in imprisonment. Yet when Mr Hartford unearthed the crown again, the brothers were re-energised and travelled to Earth intent on finding it.

The Sentinel Knight appeared to Mr Hartford, instructing him to protect the crown and its five missing jewels. To do that, Mr Hartford needed to create a team – the Power Rangers Operation Overdrive.

Mr Hartford sought to bring together a group of young and highly talented people to unite into a team. For the brains of the unit, he recruited genius-level graduate, Rose Ortiz. For its top driver, he brought in one of motor racing's most skilled performers, Ronny Robinson. To handle the physical challenges that lay in wait for the team, Mr Hartford went for one of the film world's most talented stuntmen, Dax Lo. And for all the secretive tasks he knew his team would need to accomplish, he tracked down government agent and business spy-for-hire, Will Aston.

When Mr Hartford explained to the teens why he'd called them to Hartford Mansion, they found his speech extremely far-fetched. However, Mack, Mr Hartford's son, was far more ready to believe, as he secretly listened to his father's story through the vent in the wall. I'd like to point out that I don't approve of eavesdropping and never do it myself.

It took an appeal from the Sentinel Knight to convince the four teens that becoming Power Rangers was vital to save both Earth and the entire universe. Once they were fully aware of what was at stake, they agreed to undergo DNA enhancement, giving them special powers. As the Pink Ranger, Rose was given the power of invisibility. Ronny, the Yellow Ranger, was granted super speed. Blue Ranger Dax found he had the power to bounce great heights and distances, while the power of super sight and hearing went to Will, the Black Ranger.

Mr Hartford planned to lead the team himself as the Red Ranger. However, when Moltor and his Lava Lizards attacked Hartford Mansion and the team attempted to use their Overdrive Trackers to morph into Rangers for the first time, Mr Hartford was captured. His Tracker fell to the floor and was snatched up by Mack, who used it to become the Red Ranger.

Mackenzie, to give him his full name, impressed the others in the team very much. Yet when Mr Hartford was rescued, he was at first reluctant to allow Mack to continue as the team leader, fearing for his son's safety. But when Mack and the others lobbied for it, Mack was given a second chance, and he didn't disappoint. Mr Hartford had no option but to enhance his DNA too, giving Mack super strength. However, I fear he may have given him too much, as afterwards young Mack easily picked me up with just one hand!

The search for the missing jewels is now taking the team across the globe. Long lost artefacts from ancient civilisations have been unearthed, some offering clues to the locations of the gems. To aid the search, Mr Hartford's considerable wealth has allowed him to construct a superb, hi-tech base beneath Hartford Mansion.

He has put together an impressive range of advanced vehicles for the Overdrive team to use, such as the Dump Driver, Speed Driver and Dozer Driver. Many of these can combine to form giant fighting machines, such as the mighty DriveMax Megazord.

But because the lost jewels promise such immense power to those who find them, several more villains have joined the search. Besides Flurious and Moltor, other evil aliens such as Kamdor, and his devious accomplice, Miratrix, are also chasing the gems. Unfortunately, I fear they will not be the last to join this global treasure hunt.

Nevertheless, let me conclude my first diary entry by going back to the "equally great treasure" I referred to earlier. Would it not be truly remarkable if this force of Power Rangers, complete strangers when they were first brought together, could unlock their potential to form a team of world-saving heroes?

That potential, I would suggest, is the greatest treasure this impressive group of youngsters could ever unearth, and if this happens, who knows what incredible adventures they will embark on? I just hope my nerves can stand it!

Spencer.

RED

Mack grew up wanting to go on exciting missions, just like his adventurer father. Mack's dream came true when his father finally agreed to let him become the Red Ranger!

FULL NAME:

Mackenzie 'Mack' Hartford

BRAINS   9

TOP GEAR:

Overdrive Tracker, Sentinel Morpher

SPEED   10

ZORDS:

Dump Driver, Sonic Streaker

POWER   8

OVERDRIVE RANGER

POWERS:

Super Strength

ABILITY · 10

HOBBIES:

Reading adventure stories

COOLNESS · 8

WEAPONS:

Drive Lance, Drive Defender

SKILL · 9

What overall power score will you give the Red Ranger?

10

PROFILE

As a professional spy-for-hire, Will prefers to work alone. However, as the Rangers set out on their group missions, he gradually learns the value of working as a team.

FULL NAME:
Will Aston

BRAINS   ⑨

TOP GEAR:
Overdrive Tracker, Hovertek Cycle

SPEED   ⑧

ZORDS:
Speed Driver, Crane Driver

POWER   ⑧

BLACK OVERDRIVE RANGER

POWERS:
Super Hearing, Super Sight

ABILITY   8

HOBBIES:
Cracking hi-tech security codes and safes

COOLNESS   7

WEAPONS:
Drive Slammer, Drive Defender

SKILL   8

What overall power score will you give the Black Ranger?

——— 10

BLUE

PROFILE

Dax, the Blue Ranger, was once a professional stunt person for Hollywood movies. He loved the work but Dax much prefers being a Ranger because the battle moves are for real!

FULL NAME:
Dax Lo

BRAINS 7

TOP GEAR:
Overdrive Tracker, Overdrive Motorcycle
SPEED 8

ZORDS:
Gyro Driver, Cement Driver
POWER 7

20

OVERDRIVE RANGER

POWERS:
Super Bouncing
ABILITY 8

HOBBIES:
Going to the cinema
COOLNESS 6

WEAPONS:
Drive Vortex,
Drive Defender
SKILL 7

Rate the Blue Ranger for overall power!

10

ANCIENT CROWN

The Sentinel Knight has set you a challenge. Can you trace over the lines to draw the Corona Aurora?

CORONA AURORA

BATTLE SOUNDS

Can you find these Power Rangers battle sounds in the wordsearch? Tick the blast next to each word as you find it.

Z	T	A	E	L	N	F	H	O	W
T	H	W	U	D	D	R	U	S	I
C	W	M	U	T	N	Q	X	L	C
Y	A	J	G	L	I	Y	E	B	H
S	C	W	W	O	M	M	P	P	A
X	K	S	P	C	G	U	D	I	N
P	W	F	J	V	E	L	N	H	G
T	D	M	Q	W	O	J	R	G	W
K	L	K	T	O	C	U	A	W	A
A	K	A	B	O	O	O	O	M	M

THWACK

WOMMPP

CHANG

THWUDD

KABOOOOMM

Now invent some of your own battle sounds!

Answers on page 68.

THE EASTER ISLAND TRAP

The all new **Power Rangers Operation Overdrive** team faced a big challenge when evil **Moltor** and his **Lava Lizards** attacked a wind farm!

Come on, guys! We need to protect this vital power source for the city!

THADUNNNG!

Back at Base ...

I'm worried about Mack after he took that hit ...

The **Gyro Driver** will get me to Easter Island soon enough to keep an eye on him!

Meanwhile, in Moltor's lava-pit hideout ...

The **tracking device** we hid on the Rangers' vehicle is **active**!

If they find any of the Corona Aurora jewels, **we'll be there to take them!** Prepare to teleport ...

27

Hold it! What's that – some kind of canister?

Moltor watched the Rangers with interest ...

They've found something ...

Lava Lizards! Attack and seize it!

Uh-oh! I feared this!

SWOOOP!

Just then, Moltor spotted Andrew ...

Ahh! You're just what I need!

Stop **fighting!** Let's trade, Rangers – his life for the canister!

I guess we trade?

Yeah, I'll hand the canister to Moltor ... **oops!**

Sorry. Here you go!

Ranger, you're as clumsy as him!

But after teleporting back to his hideout ...

What? It's ... **empty!**

While back at Base ...

Dropping the canister fooled Moltor. I 'palmed' its contents – a trick I learned from my book!

But ...

No! This isn't a map of jewel locations, after all. The mission was a waste of time!

Wrong! I saw what a good team you've become. And while I'll always worry about you, Mack, I've learned to keep out of your way in future!

The end

OVERDRIVE

When the five teens became Power Rangers, Andrew Hartford gave them each their own unique Driver Weapon!

DRIVE SLAMMER

This powerful hammer weapon is capable of cracking the earth's surface with a single hit!

DRIVE VORTEX

The Drive Vortex launches whirlwind air blasts and is modelled on a jet turbine engine.

DRIVE GEYSER

The Drive Geyser shoots a super-fierce, constant water stream to hold back the enemy.

DRIVE CLAWS

These sharp bulldozer claws are very strong. They can be used to throw rocks and excavate cliff faces.

WEAPONS

DRIVE LANCE

This super-tough staff has a pincer-like head with a retractable blade.

Now colour the Red Ranger holding his Drive Lance!

BADDIES PROFILE

EVIL

When rival brothers Flurious and Moltor first tried to steal the Corona Aurora, they were cursed and sent to distant planets. Now they're free again, they are more determined than ever to get their hands on the crown!

FULL NAME:
Flurious

BRAINS ⊘ ⊘ ⊘ ⊘ ⊘ ⊘ ⊘ ⊘ ⑨ ⊘ ⊘ ⊘

ELEMENT:
Ice

POWER ⊘ ⊘ ⊘ ⊘ ⑥ ⊘

ARMY:
Chillers

ABILITY ⊘ ⑥ ⊘ ⊘

BROTHERS

Which evil villain would you defeat first?

FULL NAME:

Moltor

BRAINS   7

ELEMENT:

Fire

POWER   9

ARMY:

Lava Lizards

ABILITY   7

POWER

The Black Ranger is practising his power moves. Which combination below is the most powerful? Use the key to add up the scores for each row.

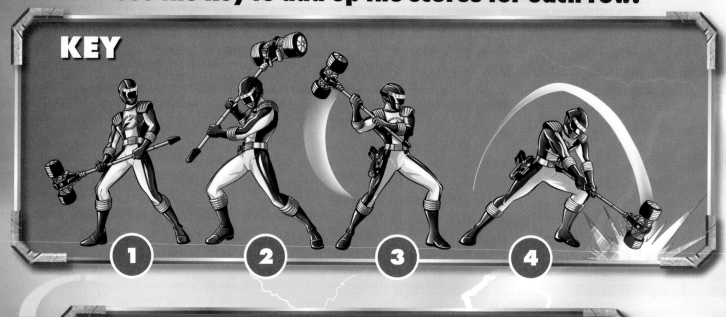

KEY

1   2   3   4

a   +   +   =   TOTAL

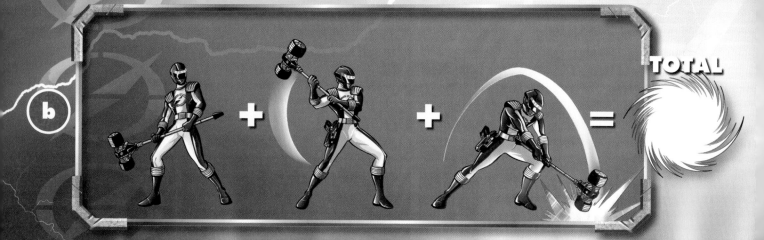

b   +   +   =   TOTAL

Answers on page 68.

MOVES

Now add some extra power to the Black Ranger's move by colouring the picture!

ICE RAIDERS

In the vast hangar underneath Hartford Mansion, the **Power Rangers Operation Overdrive** team were at the controls of their five **DriveMax** vehicles ...

Emergency scramble! Let's roll!

SSWWOOOSH!

Evil Flurious's plan had gone better than he expected ...

Ha! I knew the Ranger Base was close but they even carried us inside!

The pair quickly searched their surroundings ...

Ooh, pretty jewels!

Let me see! **Yes** – the Rangers have found **two** jewels from the Corona Aurora!

Or rather, they **had!** Mission accomplished, Norg – let's teleport away!

43

JEWEL SEARCH

Lead the Black Ranger through this icy maze, collecting as many Corona Aurora jewels as possible along the way!

START

FINISH

Which jewel couldn't the Ranger find? Colour the jewel with the right colour.

Answers on page 68.

MEGA STRENGTH

Colour the Drivemax Megazord using
the coloured dots as your guide.

Pretend to
hold a sword
like the
Drivemax
Megazord!

PROFILE

Ronny, the Yellow Ranger, is the fourth member of the team. She is a champion racing driver, so Andrew Hartford put her in charge of piloting the team's high-speed jet!

FULL NAME:

Veronica 'Ronny' Robinson

BRAINS ⊘ ⊘ ⊘ ⑥ ⊘ ⊘ ⊘

TOP GEAR:

Overdrive Tracker,
S.H.A.R.C. Jet

SPEED ⊘ ⊘ ⊘ ⊘ ⑦ ⊘ ⊘ ⊘ ⊘ ⊘ ⊘

ZORDS:

Dozer Driver, Drill Driver

POWER ⊘ ⊘ ⊘ ⊘ ⑧ ⊘ ⊘ ⊘ ⊘ ⊘ ⊘

YELLOW OVERDRIVE RANGER

POWERS:
Super Speed

ABILITY   10

HOBBIES:
Stock-car racing

COOLNESS   7

WEAPONS:
Drive Claws,
Drive Defender

SKILL   8

Rate the Yellow Ranger for overall power!

10

PROFILE

Rose is a Mensa-level genius, so she already knew the story of the Corona Aurora when Andrew recruited her as a Ranger. She'd thought it was just a myth, but before long she was fighting evil forces to protect it!

FULL NAME:
Rose Ortiz

BRAINS (10)

TOP GEAR:
Overdrive Tracker, Humvee truck

SPEED (8)

ZORDS:
Sub Driver, Shovel Driver

POWER (7)

PINK OVERDRIVE RANGER

POWERS:

Invisibility

ABILITY 9

HOBBIES:

Mythology,
reading poetry

COOLNESS 6

WEAPONS:

Drive Geyser,
Drive Defender

SKILL 6

Rate the
Pink Ranger
for overall
power!

10

51

In his volcano lair, evil Moltor also saw the news broadcast on his lava pool ...

Hmm, this Colbane interests me ...

... such a skilled treasure hunter could help me find the Corona Aurora jewels!

Later in the Overdrive base, Andrew was scanning for jewel signals ...

Got one! On **Cape West**. Hey, Colbane has a mansion there!

Rose had a theory ...

Fabergé eggs often contained fabulous jewels. Maybe the one Colbane found has a **Coruna Aurora jewel** inside!

Will set off for Cape West alone. He used his spy skills to break into Colbane's mansion ...

Top grade security, as expected. Not quite good enough, also as expected! Hmm ...

Now ... wait! I'm picking up voices downstairs with my super hearing ...

Will quickly morphed...

It's a remarkable piece, Mr Rotlom ...

And with my super eyesight, I can see ... **the Corona Aurora** itself!

And it's **been stolen!** I'll take it back **now!**

I'll check it out ...

Hey, this is just glass! Colbane's Fabergé Egg was **a fake!**

We must have picked up the **crown's** signal earlier!

Argh, I'll have revenge for this!

Later, back at Base ...

I know – I acted like a loner again ...

Hey, you saw a chance to grab back the crown and went for it, that's all.

Well, not quite all – I also saw a chance to grab this back ...

Mack's mother's necklace!

The end

PROFILE

Tyzonn is a Mercurian Intergalactic Emergency Responder. Evil Moltor transformed him into a reptile, but the Red Ranger managed to turn him back to his humanoid form using the Corona Aurora jewels. Tyzonn decided to join the Power Rangers and became the Mercury Ranger!

FULL NAME:

Tyzonn

BRAINS   7

TOP GEAR:

Mercury Morpher

SPEED   7

ZORDS:

Rescue Runners

POWER   7

MERCURY OVERDRIVE RANGER

POWERS:
Able to turn himself into liquid mercury

ABILITY ⊘ ⊘ ⊘ (9)

HOBBIES:
Fighting Fearcats!

COOLNESS ⊘ ⊘ (8)

WEAPONS:
Drive Detector

SKILL ⊘ ⊘ (6)

Rate the Mercury Ranger for overall power!

10

CALL THE

When the Rangers need extra battle power, they quickly summon the Drivemax Zords. How quickly can you complete these Zord puzzles?

1 Can you draw lines to link each Ranger with their Drivemax Zord?

Can you link the Zords' names to the right picture, too?

SPEED DRIVER
SUB DRIVER

DOZER DRIVER
DUMP DRIVER
GYRO DRIVER

ZORDS

2 See if you can find the details in the big picture of the **Dump Driver.**

c

b

a

d

e

Which two details are not from the big picture?

CHILLER CHASE

Look at the page carefully, then shut your eyes.
With a pen, try to land a dot on each of the targets!

Add up the numbers on the targets you hit and write your power score in the blast!

TEAM POWER

The five teens have powered up into Overdrive Rangers!
Can you find eight differences in the bottom picture?

Answers on page 68.

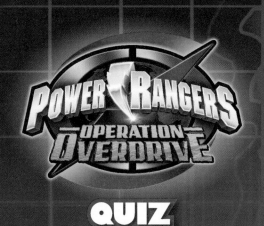

QUIZ

QUIZ

Have you got what it takes to be an Overdrive Ranger? Find out with this quiz! Tick the box next to your answer.

1 What is the name of the Ranger's leader?

Andrew Hartford ☐

Andrew Crawford ☐

2 Who is the butler at Hartford Mansion?

William ☐

Spencer ☐

3 Which Ranger can become invisible?

 ☐ ☐ ☐ ☐

4 How are Flurious and Moltor related?

Brothers ☐

Father and son ☐

5 Which weapon is called the Drive Slammer?

☐  ☐

CHALLENGE

6 Which of these Zords is called the Dump Driver?

7 Which of these warriors is called a Lava Lizard?

8 What is the name of the crown which the Rangers are trying to protect?

Carina Aurora

Corona Aurora

9 Which Ranger pilots the Rangers' S.H.A.R.C. vehicle?

10 What is the name of Flurious's snowman assistant?

Norg

Boom

Now check the answers on page 68.

ANSWERS

PAGE 23 BATTLE SOUNDS

Z	T	A	E	L	N	F	H	O	W
T	H	W	U	D	D	R	U	S	I
C	W	M	U	T	N	Q	X	L	C
Y	A	J	G	L	I	Y	E	B	H
S	C	W	O	M	M	P	P	A
X	K	S	P	C	G	U	D	I	N
P	W	F	J	V	E	L	N	H	G
T	D	M	Q	W	O	J	R	G	W
K	L	K	T	O	C	U	A	W	A
A	K	A	B	O	O	O	O	M	M

PAGE 36 POWER MOVES

Row 'b' shows the most powerful combination of power moves.

PAGE 46 JEWEL SEARCH

START

FINISH

The Black Ranger couldn't find the yellow jewel.

PAGE 62-63 CALL THE ZORDS

1.

2. Details 'a' and 'e' are not from the picture.

PAGE 65 TEAM POWER

PAGE 66-67 QUIZ CHALLENGE

For every correct answer, award yourself one point.

1 - Andrew Hartford; 2 - Spencer; 3 - Pink Ranger; 4 - Brothers; 5 - the long, hammer-like weapon; 6 - the red vehicle; 7 - the red warrior holding a black sword; 8 - Corona Aurora; 9 - Yellow Ranger; 10 - Norg.

RANGER RATING:

0-3: Hmm, you need to do a little more training
4-7: You show real Ranger potential. Good work
8-10: Well done! The Rangers want you on their team!

Have you seen Power Rangers magazine?

Available from all good newsagents and supermarkets.

Out every 3 week-!